Saint Odelia

Through Darkness and into the Light

Saint Odelia

Through Darkness and into the Light

by

Jakob Streit

Translated by Nina Kuettel

Illustrations by Martina Müller

Waldorf
PUBLICATIONS

Printed with support from the Waldorf Curriculum Fund

Published by:
Waldorf Publications at the
Research Institute for Waldorf Education
38 Main Street
Chatham, NY 12037

Title: *Saint Odelia*
       Through Darkness and into the Light
Author: Jakob Streit
Translator: Nina Kuettel
Editor: David Mitchell
Illustrator: Martina Müller
Copy Editor and Proofreader: Ann Erwin
Cover: David Mitchell

© 2010 by AWSNA
ISBN # 978-1-936367-05-4

Original German title: *Die heilige Odilie, Durch Finsternis zum Licht*
Publisher: Urachhaus, 1997
ISBN # 3-8251-7154-X

Table of Contents

The Grim Duke

In the Alsace region of France, on a ridge in the Vosges Mountains, stood a proud castle called Hohenburg. It was surrounded by strong, protective walls. A tower rose high into the sky. One evening Etichon, the Duke of Alsace, and some hunters were riding toward the ridge. Two of the men were carrying their hunting kill hanging from a long stick. It was a powerful elk! Its legs were bound to the stick at the knees so that its antlers would not hang too low and drag on the ground. Blood dripped from the wounds. Fierce hunting dogs surrounded the men, barking wildly. One dog licked up some of the blood right away. Next to the Duke rode his hunting companion, Ulrich. He had wounded the elk with an arrow so that the Duke could kill it with his lance.

While they were riding, Ulrich said to the Duke: "I had a good day today. Early in the morning my wife brought a son into the world, and it was my arrow, from a good distance, that brought that elk to the ground." Ulrich chuckled with pride.

To his surprise no word of praise came from Etichon. Instead the Duke suddenly spurred his horse and rode to the front, alone. The man riding behind Ulrich said to him: "You have made the Duke doubly angry. You know that he has been waiting for years for his wife, Bereswinde, to give him a son. But up to now she has borne him no child. Your fatherly pride has offended him. And that you were the first to hit the elk – you should not have rubbed it in like that."

Ulrich responded: "His anger will go up in smoke tonight when we have the elk on a spit and ale and wine to drink. The traveling bard will chase away his bad mood with cheerful songs."

From a window in the tower Bereswinde, the Duchess, had seen her husband riding at the front of the hunting party and coming closer to the castle. She combed her blonde hair, smoothed out her silk dress, and hurried down to the castle gate to greet him. As Etichon rode through the high gate, he looked grim; he had no word for his wife. He rode by without even looking at her. Bereswinde was used to Etichon's bad moods. She was well aware what the worry was for both of them: A castle lord without an heir! Sadly, she returned to her chambers.

That evening in the great hall a fire crackled in the huge fireplace. Candles from two lamps made from elk antlers spread a soft light in the room. The long table was set, and the wine cups were filled. Talking loudly among themselves, the hunters took their places at the table. Only one was missing, the Duke.

Ulrich commanded the bard to prepare to sing, and he said: "I will go get Etichon. The hunt was difficult. He is probably resting. Ready the horns. When he comes, welcome the elk-killer with trumpets and cheers!"

It was a while before Ulrich returned with the Duke. The antlers had been separated from the elk's head, and one of the hunters held these trophies high in the air. Trumpeters stood on either side. The elk's head was made to keep time with the music as the Duke entered. His face lit up, and the group led him to the table and the chair with his coat of arms carved on it. Soon the wine cups were raised in toast. Servants carried in the roasted elk meat on copper platters. The bard played his harp and sang a hunting song:

Set out on the happy hunt,
The morning is rising.
The dogs bark, the horses neigh,
Throngs of weapons are flashing.
Soon we will ride over hill and dale,
Heiya, heiya!
Wild boar and elk,
The hunt is beautiful!
Heiya, heiya!

The singer knew a lot more verses, and the hunters joined in on the refrain in a booming chorus.

Waiting for the Baby's Birth

One day Bereswinde was pleased to tell her husband that she was expecting a child. He said to her: "At last it will be fulfilled that you will bring into the world an heir to our Hohenburg dukedom. Every day you must eat an acorn from the fruit of the oak tree. Then you will birth a strong boy."

The Duke knew a lot about pagan customs. Christianity had made very little headway with him. He was from the Merovingian family, and they were known for their harsh ways.

The months passed. As the hour of the birth came for Bereswinde, Etichon was out hunting wild boar. The loyal midwife, Berta, soon cradled the child in its mother's arms. "But," she said softly, "it is a girl." Bereswinde took the baby and was filled with love. At the same time, a shiver went through her when she thought of Etichon. What would he say?

In the evening the lord of the castle and his men returned with their bounty from the hunt. The guard at the gate told them the news: "My Lord Duke, a daughter was born to you this day."

Etichon's face twisted in anger. He got down from his horse in the courtyard and angrily hit a wooden post with his sword so hard that it split in two. Then he disappeared into the cellar. He tapped a wine barrel and poured cup after cup down his burning throat. Still angry, he smashed the cellar door. He hotly demanded that a horse be saddled for him. He galloped away from the castle down into the forest. He was gone for days. Nobody knew where he went.

The Girl Is Blind

On the second day, when Berta, the nursemaid, was washing the baby girl again, she noticed that her eyes were still closed. No amount of washing helped. The baby was blind. She took the little one to her mother: "Dear Lady Duchess, maybe her eyes will open later, but right now, she is blind."

Full of sympathy, Bereswinde took the little one in her arms, looked at the delicate little face, and kissed her closed eyelids. A shiver of fear quaked through her arms when she thought of Etichon. A chamber maid had also noticed the child's blindness, and soon everyone at Hohenburg knew it too.

The Duke returned after some days, a little calmer, but still in a dark mood. He avoided the newborn child. Ulrich, the cavalry captain, thought it was right to report to Etichon about the girl's blindness. When they were seated together, Ulrich said: "Etichon, I understand your great disappointment, but Bereswinde will certainly give you a son someday. But you must know what nobody else will tell you: The newborn is blind."

The Duke pressed his teeth together so hard that they made a grinding noise. For a moment he stared straight ahead. Then he slowly pressed out these words: "It is an old German custom that the father will decide if a newborn child may live. Now I say: No."

He stood and went upstairs to Bereswinde's chambers. He stopped a moment outside the door as if he were trying to gather his courage, and he loosened the dagger from his belt.

From inside came the sound of quiet singing. Bereswinde was lying on a couch, humming a melody, gently rocking the baby in a cradle. There was a knock at the door.

Etichon stepped inside, holding the dagger behind his back. He ordered: "Give me that blind creature. It may not be allowed to live as a disgrace to us!"

Bereswinde grabbed the baby from the cradle, pressed her to her, and stood up straight. Her eyes were flashing. "You will not hurt this child, or I die with her!" She raised her right hand in a gesture of authority and repelled Etichon. He had never seen his wife act so forcefully, or look so beautiful. They stood opposite each other as if frozen.

Slowly, Etichon put the dagger back in his belt. He withdrew step by step. His heavy footfalls echoed down the stairs. The door stood open. The baby's guardian angel had given Bereswinde the courage and strength to stand against Etichon.

Bereswinde settled the child back in the cradle. As if she were waking up from a bad dream, she let her tears fall unhindered. That is how Berta found her mistress.

A Plan Is Foiled

That same evening Etichon and Ulrich were sitting together. Squire Ulrich was really the only person Etichon trusted. A fire flickered in the open fireplace.

Etichon broke the silence: "I could not do what I wanted to do today, get rid of that miserable creature. It has to happen secretly. I am putting it to you, Ulrich, as my trusted friend, to undertake this task. It is up to you how it will be done. A thread of life that is barely spun is easily broken. Outside in the forest the belladonna is ripe. With a few drops of poison, a weak life can be easily brushed away, without blood. I should think that in the next few days you can be done with it. You may choose: dagger or poison. What do you think?"

Ulrich replied: "Lord, I am in your debt. Just a short time ago you gifted me the black horse. Your wish is my command!"

Etichon was not yet satisfied: "There is one thing I require. Neither from you nor anyone else do I ever again want to hear anything about this creature. I want to erase it from my memory! Is it a deal?" The Duke offered his hand, and Ulrich shook it.

In the great hall, the dinner after the day's hunting lasted late into the night. In Bereswinde's chambers during this time another plan was being spun. The Duchess knew well that Etichon would try to find a way to get rid of the child. Berta, the nursemaid, had parents who lived a day's ride away, in a cottage tucked away in the forest. They barely made a living from rocky fields and a few animals. The Duchess spoke to Berta: "Early in the morning, when it is daylight, take my child. Please, help me to save her. We will bed her down in a basket with a lid, and you will secretly carry her out of the castle. If someone should ask where you are going, tell them: 'I am fetching some things for Bereswinde.' Go back to your parents, and keep her there in secret. I will give you some gold and silver money so that you and the child will not be in need for anything. With God's help she will grow up. When she is a little older, take her to the good nuns at the convent. They will gladly take in a blind girl." The two women talked about their plan a little while longer, and then Berta retired to her bed.

Sometime after midnight Bereswinde was startled awake when she heard creaking noises on the wooden stairs. She listened. The moon dimly lit up her room. All was quiet for a while, but then the door opened softly. Bereswinde sat up and called: "Who is there?!" A shadow disappeared and the stairs creaked again. The door was still open.

Bereswinde closed it and barred it from the inside. She sank back in her bed, very tired. She knew that someone had tried to steal her child. She got up again and went to the cradle. The baby was sleeping. She folded her hands and prayed. And grace and mercy were shown to her. In a beam of light she saw an image, and two blessing hands were over the cradle, and then the vision disappeared. But Bereswinde was sure: "My little girl is well protected and will be guided." She was filled with deep happiness, comforted to know that her daughter would be watched over.

The Flight to Safety

Early in the morning the two women wrapped the baby girl in a soft blanket and tucked her in a cushioned basket. She had already been fed so she slept soundly. Bereswinde gave Berta a little purse with coins in it, and Berta hid it in the bottom of the basket. The basket was closed with a woven lid which allowed air still to get inside. Bereswinde hugged Berta. There were tears in her eyes, but she held herself together.

The castle gate was open and the guards were eating breakfast in the servant's kitchen. Nobody noticed the path Berta took. She walked quickly down the hill. She was not quite to the valley when she set the basket down on the edge of the path to take a short rest. She heard horses' hooves coming closer from the castle. It was the Duke and Ulrich. No escape was possible. The riders saw Berta with the basket and they halted. Berta felt faint.

Ulrich asked: "Where are you going?"

Berta stood in front of the basket and in a strong voice replied: "I am fetching some things for Bereswinde!"

Ulrich said with a grin: "Don't fill your basket too full of vegetables. Going uphill is harder!" The Duke made a dismissive gesture with his hand, spurred his horse, and they were gone. Berta's legs were shaking. She sat down and silently thanked Providence for her good luck. A side path led her into the forest and further toward her destination.

Berta had married at a young age, but her husband had been killed in an accident while cutting down a tree. Her parents had cared for her only child so that she could become a midwife and nursemaid at the castle to earn a simple living. She was very happy that she would soon see her son, Sigo, again. She thought that in one or two years, he and the blind girl could enjoy playing together.

But the little girl did not have a name yet! As Berta was walking along, trying to think of a good name, it came to her: Bewinda is her name, similar to her mother's name. The further Berta traveled away from the castle, the more lighthearted she felt.

Suddenly she heard footsteps. A pilgrim appeared, in a long robe and carrying a wanderer's staff. Berta wanted to greet him briefly and then continue on her way, but he stopped her. He greeted her with: "Praised be to Jesus Christ!" He explained: "I travel from monastery to monastery and help Irish monks plant their gardens. But my longest stay was near a convent called Palma. Very devoted women have settled there. I was a cowherd there for some time. If you are looking for a peaceful place to settle, go to Palma. It is about two days' traveling time from here. But I have wanderer's blood, so I will travel on through the land."

Berta thanked him for the good advice, but she wanted to keep going before the child in the basket made a noise. Who knew if the pilgrim might not visit Hohenburg and tell about their meeting?

It was wonderful how little Bewinda slept. Once, while Berta was resting, she peeked inside the basket and thought she was looking upon a sleeping angel.

Late in the afternoon Berta arrived at her parents' forest cottage. They hardly had time for a greeting before the hungry voice of the baby in the basket was heard. Berta opened the lid. Her mother looked inside with amazement, and asked: "Who is this? What child is this? It has its eyes closed and is crying. I've never seen a baby cry with its eyes closed like it's asleep."

Berta explained: "The little one is blind. She will never be able to open her eyes."

As soon as the baby was fed, Berta told the whole, long story. She ended with these words: "Above all, nobody may ever find out that this child belongs to the Duke of Hohenburg, or I don't know what would happen. Please forget this story! She is now *my* child, Bewinda, sister to Sigo."

Berta's parents welcomed Bewinda into their hearts. So she grew up in the little cottage next to the forest meadow with a cow, sheep, goats, and Sigo, who was a good brother and playmate.

Time went by. At Hohenburg, as the Duke had ordered, nobody ever spoke about the missing blind girl. They also did not try to guess who had killed her. Bereswinde gave birth to a son named Hugo, and Etichon was very proud of him. The boy was already a good rider. But Hugo's heart was devoted to his mother. Bereswinde told him fairytales and stories about knights, and also about a wondrous man in faraway Palestine. Sometimes an Irish monk would visit Hohenburg, and Bereswinde would ask him to stay awhile and teach Hugo. So, Hugo learned to write and read, and he enjoyed singing while the monk played the harp.

Etichon did not appreciate these things very much. He taught Hugo how to use weapons and to hunt.

Bewinda Is Taken to Palma

Over the years Bewinda grew into a pretty, healthy girl. She was a friend to the animals. She combed the goats, played with the lambs and kittens, and brushed the cow. When the roses were blooming in the cottage garden, Berta would watch the girl kneel down to breathe in the perfume and tenderly caress the blossoms. If she pricked her finger on a thorn, she would wince a little, but was soon smiling again. She said to Berta: "Do you know what the roses say to me? They say: Come slowly and softly up to a rosebush. We punish hasty, rough hands!" Berta laughed.

But Bewinda had so many questions: How are roses made? Where does the rain come from? Why is fire so hot? Who made the sun? Why do people die? Where do their souls go? Are there very many other people in the world? Berta knew that she did not have the answers to so many questions. She thought about the wise women at the Palma Convent. Surely they would know. So Berta became more certain that she should take Bewinda to Palma. Bewinda would learn a lot from the good nuns, and she would be cared for in her later life.

When the new spring arrived, those living in the forest cottage celebrated Bewinda's ninth birthday. Her grandmother gave her a white dress for her birthday that she had made from spun and woven wool. Berta said to her: "Bewinda, we are going to take a walk together, to other people."

Bewinda was so happy! As Berta was tying the strings on their bundle of things for the trip, Bewinda asked: "May Sigo come along? He is always so good at leading me by the hand."

Berta replied: "He has to stay here to look after the animals in the pasture. I can't ask your elderly grandfather to take on more work. But I will lead you safely."

Bewinda asked again: "Once you told me a story about a castle. Are we going to a castle? May I talk to the knights?"

"We are going to a big house where there are kind women who sing very beautifully."

"May I sing with them? Will they teach me new songs?"

"Yes, if we are able to stay with them for a while, you may sing with them. They will know the answers to the many questions you have. They have clever heads. You can learn a lot there. "

"Are clever heads very large?"

"Their heads are no larger than ours. But there is light in them." Bewinda was silent, thinking about heads filled with light.

In private, Berta spoke to her parents: "I will probably stay awhile with Bewinda at the Palma Convent, until she gets used to things. She will be well looked after there. After all, she is the child of a Duke!"

When the two of them said good-bye, the kind grandmother was crying. Bewinda said: "Grandmother, don't cry! Be happy that I am able to travel. This morning I saw two lights in a dream. They came closer and closer together. And then there was one great light that shone bright inside of me. Isn't that a wonderful dream for the start of our journey?"

Sigo, who did not know what was really happening, called out: "Bring me back something nice!"

Hand in hand, Berta and Bewinda walked through the forest. In a meadow valley was a small settlement of huts where they spent the night. The farmers shared generously with them. Berta gave them a coin from the purse she had received from the Duchess. She had used very little of the money. She wanted to give it to the nuns at Palma if they would allow Bewinda to stay. The next morning the farmers pointed them in the right direction.

Toward evening on the third day of their journey, they arrived at the convent. The small bell in the chapel was just ringing to call everyone to prayer. "What is that lovely sound?" Bewinda asked. "Can an animal make such a beautiful noise?"

"No, that is the bell in the chapel at the convent. It swings back and forth, and then it rings."

"Is it alive? Can one pet it?"

"No, it is made from metal, just like a warrior's sword."

"Wonderful! But it doesn't kill?"

"No, it rings to call the sisters to prayer. It rings for peace." The little bell stopped.

Berta and Bewinda entered the courtyard of the convent. They could hear singing coming from the chapel. The door was open a crack. Berta went very close with Bewinda and whispered: "The nuns are having a church service."

Bewinda was overwhelmed by the singing. She had never heard anything so beautiful. She wrapped her arms around Berta, and tears fell from her closed eyes. One of the sisters who had arrived late opened the door and made a sign that they were to enter the chapel. The tired wanderers took their places on a bench furthest in the back. Words were said, then singing again. Bewinda felt she was in a wonderful dream. Her face beamed with happiness.

The service came to an end. Berta asked to speak with the Abbess in charge of the convent; she had a request to make. One of the sisters led them inside the convent and announced their visit. Reverend Mother Irmgard, the Abbess, gave them a friendly greeting. But her gaze remained on the child. What a beautiful face!

"What is your name, child? The Abbess was filled with sympathy.

"Bewinda," came the answer, in a clear voice.

"Come closer, Bewinda. Give me your hands!"

Berta led Bewinda closer to the Abbess. Abbess Irmgard took her tender hands. Suddenly, the girl asked: "Did you sing along? It was beautiful, like in a dream!"

"Then you must have wonderful dreams, Bewinda! You both have a long journey behind you. Come, have some food and drink." After these words the Abbess picked up a small hand bell and rang it.

"Oh, how lovely!" said Bewinda.

A sister appeared. Abbess Irmgard said: "Brigida, take the child with you and give her milk and bread. Her mother will come a little later!" Full of trust, Bewinda held out her hand for the nun and followed her.

The Conversation

When she was alone with Abbess Irmgard, Berta began: "Reverend Mother, I am not the mother of the blind child. My name is Berta, and I am a simple farmer's daughter. But the girl is the unwanted child of a royal family. I need your advice and your help!"

Then Berta told about her employment with Bereswinde, wife to the Duke of Hohenburg. She described the rough life at the castle, and the Duke's long wait for a son, an heir. Instead of a son, the blind girl was born. "When the Duke, in his anger, wanted to have the baby killed, Bereswinde gave the child to me to save her life. I left the castle with her in secret and have raised her in isolation at my parents' home. I heard about the convent here, and the kindness and mercy that you have shown. Dear Reverend Mother, could you take the child in and help her to be accepted into the circle of nuns here?"

Berta grew silent. The Abbess sank her head in thought. When she looked up again, she said: "A little angel has come to us. Yes, the child may stay with us. But for a short time, you, Berta, should stay with her until she becomes familiar with things here. "

Berta took the Abbess's hand in gratitude and kissed it. Then she searched in her travel pack until she found the money purse, and said: "Duchess Bereswinde gave me this purse so that the child would not suffer any need." She shook the contents onto the table. It glittered with gold and silver coins.

Irmgard's eyes grew wide, for Palma was a poor convent. She said: "We would have taken the dear child even without money. But now, we can finally buy a horse and wagon, and other things we have needed for a long time. What a happy day!"

When the evening bell rang, calling them to the chapel, Bewinda sat between Berta and Brigida, who had given her milk, bread, and butter. Bewinda hummed along softly with the singing. She had quickly become friends with Brigida. The Abbess asked Brigida to look after Bewinda like a mother.

Bewinda was happy to stay with the sisters. Her quick mind easily learned the songs for the church services. As her teacher, Brigida read her stories about the life of Jesus Christ. One time Bewinda asked: "Where do you get the beautiful songs that we sing in the chapel?"

Brigida explained: "Many of them are originally from Ireland, the green island in the ocean. There was a shepherd there named Cadmon. When he was alone in the green hills, tending his sheep, he would often think about the beginnings of all the wonderful things in nature. The sun, moon, stars, clouds, and wind were his friends. He heard stories at a monastery about the creation of the world. And he heard about the life and death of Christ. In the days that followed, up on the moor, songs and poems began to pour out of him. If he was with the sheep, he would often sing for hours about everything he had heard.

"A nun, who was out gathering herbs, heard him. She reported to the Abbess about the singing shepherd. The Abbess had him brought to her, and he sang so beautifully that she gave him a harp. Another nun taught him how to play it. Another shepherd took over watching the sheep, and Cadmon went traveling from place to place as a wandering singer. When he sang in monasteries and convents, a scribe would write down his songs. Many of the songs that we sing here in Palma come from Cadmon, the Christian singer and bard."

Bewinda also learned from Brigida how to do simple handwork like spinning wool and flax.

A few days later when Berta asked Bewinda if she would like to stay in Palma, she replied: "Dear Mother, I am so happy to be able to stay here. But, please, come to visit me sometimes and, whenever you can, bring my dear brother, Sigo, with you. He was always so nice to me."

Berta felt lighthearted as she journeyed the two days back home. She was certain that Bewinda's guardian angel had led her to Palma. While she was walking Berta thought that one day she should visit the castle at Hohenburg and comfort the Duchess with the news that her daughter was in good hands. But she was still afraid of the Duke. He might recognize her and try to take revenge on her.

Bewinda Becomes Odelia

All this time, in faraway Regensburg, there lived a Bishop Ehrhard. Through his life of devotion he had reached the point that sometimes visions would come to him. One night while he was praying, an angel appeared to him, and he heard the voice: "Ehrhard, go to Palma in the Vosges Mountains. You will find a maiden there who has been blind since birth. Baptize her with the name Odelia. She will receive a miracle." The vision of light disappeared.

The very next day Ehrhard and one of his monastery brothers started on the journey. Ehrhard had never heard of the convent at Palma, but he did know about the Vosges Mountains far to the west. It was a long walk up along the Danube River, but Ehrhard clearly understood that one must carry out spiritual orders. When he and his brother monk got to the Black Forest, they were able to get directions to the Palma Convent.

Upon his arrival, Bishop Ehrhard was taken directly to the Abbess. She greeted the travelers with surprise at the great distance they had come. He explained what had brought him to Palma and asked about the blind girl. Abbess Irmgard had Sister Brigida bring Bewinda. The girl stood before the important gentleman, full of expectation. He greeted her in a fatherly way. Ehrhard was impressed by the girl's beauty — her finely formed face, her golden-blonde hair, her straight posture. He began the conversation by asking: "What is the most enjoyable work for you here in the convent?"

Without any shyness, Bewinda answered: "I like to spin. And when the spindle turns, I like to sing softly along with it."

"What kind of songs do you sing?"

"Sister Brigida taught me some Psalms, but sometimes I just sing whatever comes to mind."

"What songs come to mind?"

"I sing whole stories that Brigida has told me: about the creation of the world and about Jacob and the ladder to Heaven that the angels went up and down and comforted him. I sing about Miriam, the sister of Moses. She was there when the Hebrew people went through the Red Sea and were saved. I also sing about David, the shepherd boy, how he overcame Goliath. And, I like to sing about Daniel in the lion's den, and how no lion attacked him!"

Ehrhard smiled, and was happy about the girl's lively spirit. But then he grew serious and said: "Bewinda, come here and give me both your hands. Did Brigida tell you about John the Baptist?" Bewinda nodded. Ehrhard continued: "He baptized people in the water of the Jordan River so that their spirits would awaken to receive the new Gospel. I have come here to baptize you, tomorrow, just like John the Baptist did. Then you will be given a second, a new name. Would you like that, Bewinda?"

"As you wish it, honored Father, so shall it be. Is it a long walk to the Jordan River?"

Abbess Irmgard explained: "My dear Bewinda, in our little church there is a side chapel, and inside is a fountain where one can be baptized. You will wear a special dress for baptism and step down into the water. The priest will say the blessing and pour holy water over your head three times. Then he will give you your new name. Brigida will give you further instructions so that your soul is prepared for the baptism, and everything will go smoothly tomorrow. All of our sisters will help to decorate the church with flowers, and they will all be there for the celebration."

At this time, white lilies were blooming in the convent gardens. Early in the morning the nuns decorated the church with them. When the sun rose, the bells rang. Those taking part in the baptism, Bishop Ehrhard in front with the Abbess, escorted Bewinda to the church. Wearing a white dress, and holding Brigida's hand, Bewinda walked barefoot to the chapel. After the bells stopped ringing, three sisters began to sing and play a harp. The perfume of the lilies was mixed with the honey-sweet smell of beeswax candles. Only dim light came into the room through two small windows. Bishop Ehrhard said a prayer and asked for the blessings of angels to be poured out on Bewinda. Brigida guided the girl to the baptismal fountain. A beam of light was shining onto the lilies through the tiny windows. Still holding Brigida's hand, Bewinda stepped down into the water. While the harp was played softly, Ehrhard spoke the words of baptism and poured water onto Bewinda's head three times. The words echoed:

Odelia, I baptize you in the name of the Father God.
Odelia, I baptize you in the name of His Son, Jesus Christ.
Odelia, I baptize you in the name of the Holy, Healing Spirit.

Then the miracle happened: A shiver went through Odelia. Tears pressed out of her eyes. Slowly, her eyelids opened. She was looking at a bright light. She saw the white of the lilies. She held on tight to Brigida's hand, closed her eyes again, and climbed up the steps. Before the Bishop, she sank to her knees. He laid his hands on her head in a blessing. Odelia slowly opened her eyes again. Bishop Ehrhard looked into their deep-blue depth. He took her hands and helped her stand up. Brigida hugged her and put a lily stem in her hand. Odelia stared at the white flower with gold color on the inside. "Oh!" she whispered, "Lily, you are so pretty!"

Ehrhard's heart was full. He stepped to the altar with Odelia and announced: "Dear sisters, everyone gathered here, an angel of God has granted a miracle to our Odelia. Her blind eyes have been opened! Many weeks ago in Regensburg it was foretold to me in a vision what would happen here today. At her baptism, Odelia was given her sight through God's blessing. Let us sing a song of praise and joy!"

Abbess Irmgard went to Odelia. She spread a warm shawl over her shoulders and whispered: "Now you may shake hands with all the sisters."

At a sign from the Abbess, one by one the nuns walked to her while still singing. Odelia was still holding the lily in her left hand, and she greeted each of the sisters with her right hand. Until this moment she had known them only by their voices. Now she saw all of their happy faces. When the song ended, Ehrhard said: "Let us carry a song of gratitude out into God's nature. Everyone bring a lily! We will guide Odelia into the beautiful summer world. But first, put a cloth over her head. The daylight will be too bright for her."

Brigida removed her scarf and put it over Odelia's head and face. A column of singing nuns left the chapel. They walked through the blooming meadows and gardens, and then back to the convent. Odelia stood still for a moment in front of the entrance. Here she smelled the fragrance of roses. She wanted to see the flowers that she had so often held in her hands. She lifted the scarf from her face. "Oh, what incredible color!" she cried.

"That is red," Brigida explained.

Odelia continued: "Now I see the thorns that protect the roses from rough hands." Brigida picked a rose, broke off the thorns and handed it to Odelia to carry with the lily.

It was dark in the convent when Sister Nora took the scarf from her head. Odelia looked around the room in amazement. There was the long table set for dinner and decorated with flowers of every color. Abbess Irmgard, who had come in with Bishop Ehrhard, took Odelia's hand once again, and said: "The baptized one shall sit between Bishop Ehrhard and me at the head of the table. Brigida, you may sit on the other side of the Bishop. Today is a day of celebration and jubilation!"

Odelia Experiences the Beautiful World

After a modest meal, Brigida led Odelia to her room where she could have quiet and rest. She put the rose and lily into a vase next to the bed. Odelia soon fell into a refreshing sleep.

The time for the evening service was drawing near and Brigida went to Odelia's room. At the sound of soft knocking on her door, the sleeping girl awakened. Her two wide-open, blue eyes looked at the person entering the room. In a gentle voice Odelia asked: "Where am I?"

"It is Brigida, Odelia. I have come to fetch you for the evening service. Soon the bell will ring."

Odelia gazed mutely at the flowers. As if she were still dreaming, she reached her hand for them but did not touch them: "Rose red, lily white," she whispered.

"Get up, Odelia! Listen, the bell is ringing. Look here, the Abbess has sent you a new dress, woven especially for you as a baptismal gift." Brigida helped her put on the dress: "It is made from the wool from our sheep."

"Oh, I wish to thank the sheep who gave me their wool. But who did the spinning and weaving?"

"You spun it, and Sister Hilda did the weaving and sewing."

"Then I will also thank Sister Hilda. You are all so good to me."

Bishop Ehrhard and Abbess Irmgard were waiting below. They put Odelia between them.

Odelia was already able to go outside without the little blue scarf. In front of the chapel, she looked up and smiled. She saw the church bell swinging back and forth. She said: "How happy the little bell is. It dances around, even without legs!"

A plate of bread and a pitcher of wine were set on the altar, between the candles. Bishop Ehrhard celebrated Holy Communion. Odelia was allowed to be the first to receive communion, and then the Abbess, and then the whole group of nuns.

During silent prayer, a deep stillness lay over the little church. Afterward, there was harp music and singing. The sun was setting as they all left the chapel. The clouds flamed in a beautiful, fiery blaze. Odelia was rooted to the spot, her eyes drinking in the colors. She quietly asked Brigida: "Are sun angels coloring the clouds?"

"Yes, it seems so. Look! The golden sun now appears blood-red under the lowest clouds, as it is sinking in the distance."

Odelia stood with the other sisters and stared until the fiery ball had disappeared. She was speechless. On this evening her soul was filled with the wonders of the world.

Later that night, when Odelia was asleep, Ehrhard, his traveling companion, the Abbess, and Brigida were all sitting together. Ehrhard said: "What happened with Odelia today, this miracle, has greater significance than just for Palma and all of us here who experienced it. It is important for all of Christianity. But, it will be better for the maiden if we do not tell the world about it right away. She would be overwhelmed, and she would lose her youth. Her eyes are awestruck with the beauty of the world, nature, and all of creation. If I am not mistaken, she will one day be a great help to many people."

After a few days Bishop Ehrhard and the monk said their goodbyes with much gratitude. His mission in Palma had been fulfilled.

A Visit from Berta

A year passed. Odelia blossomed more and more. She learned to write and read. She especially liked to help care for sisters who were ill. Every so often sick people were brought to the convent from the surrounding area. Odelia was glad to be allowed to help take care of them. It had been noticed that she had healing hands. She could relieve pain and lift up sad, broken-hearted souls.

One day, back in the secluded forest where they lived, Berta said to her son, Sigo: "The autumn work is done. Finally, we can take a trip to the convent at Palma and see how things are going for Bewinda." Berta did not know anything of the miracle that had happened. Her mother and father would take the few animals to the meadow every day and do the milking for a week, but the other chores they would leave. Sigo was happy. He had missed his dear sister, Bewinda!

They arrived in Palma two days later. It was already getting toward evening when Berta called on the Abbess. She and her son were given a joyful welcome. After Abbess Irmgard had sent for refreshments, she spoke to the two guests: "Bewinda received a new name when she was baptized at age twelve. She is now called Odelia. On the day of her baptism God revealed a miracle in her: After the baptism her eyes were opened. She was blessed with a Divine gift. She will be so happy about your visit! She is most likely in the scriptorium. I will send someone to bring her here."

Shortly, Odelia appeared in the doorway with radiant eyes. Berta walked toward her slowly, as if under a spell. But Odelia flew into her arms: "Dearest Mother!" Berta was overcome. Tears flowed down her cheeks. Odelia saw that they were tears of joy, tears of love. She said: "Look, Mother, the blind Bewinda has become the seeing Odelia. You brought me here. I owe you thanks for all the good things you have done for me." Once again, she hugged the joyous Berta.

Then, Odelia glimpsed her brother Sigo standing in the back of the room. She cried: "Sigo, you loyal brother!" and she hugged him as well.

Abbess Irmgard beamed with happiness. She said: "Odelia, show your loved ones around the convent – the weaving and spinning rooms and the scriptorium. Take them through the garden and show them the baptismal fountain where you received a blessing from Heaven." The Abbess took Berta to one side for a moment and added softly: "When you have seen everything, come back to me here. Odelia should now learn the truth about her birth."

Odelia took her mother and Sigo by the hand. She showed them all the places where the nuns were diligently at work. Then she guided their steps to the chapel. A cross with a sun-ring made from plaited grasses stood on the altar. They went to the side chapel with the baptismal fountain. There was no water in it. Odelia beckoned Berta and Sigo to sit. "Here," she said, "is where my eyes were opened." She began to sing softly. Berta understood something about praise and thanksgiving, words about the beautiful world, and even about sheep, cows, birds, butterflies, clouds, and colors of sunshine.

As the song ended, Berta said: "Abbess Irmgard asked that we return to her when we are finished here." Soon the three were sitting in a large room with the Abbess. Odelia wondered: *What does she want with us? She is so serious, and Mother is silent.*

Finally, Abbess Irmgard began: "Odelia, human lives hold many mysteries and secrets. Ways and detours lead mankind's children to their destinies. You love Berta who has raised you like a mother. You love Sigo as a brother, who has grown up with you. But, today, you shall learn that dear Berta is not your real mother. Your mother lives at the Castle Hohenburg. She is the Duchess, and your father is Duke Etichon."

The Abbess paused. She saw that Odelia was staring into the distance. Then she turned her gaze to Sigo, who was also hearing this news for the first time. His eyes were on the floor. Odelia whispered quietly: "Then, I have no brother?" Her eyes filled with tears.

"Not at all," said Berta. "Sigo is your foster brother, and I am your foster mother. We love you through and through." She stood up and wrapped her arms around Odelia.

Abbess Irmgard continued: "Odelia, I hear that you have a brother at Hohenburg by the name of Hugo. Is it not wonderful to have two mothers and two brothers?"

Odelia asked: "But why was I not allowed to stay at the castle?"

Abbess Irmgard answered: "Berta will now tell you how it was."

Odelia heard how the Duke, her father, could not deal with her blindness. He wanted the child out of his sight. "So your mother, Bereswinde, took me in her confidence, and I brought you to our quiet cottage in the forest. But now the time has come for you to get to know your parents and your brother Hugo. Odelia, when you were singing in the chapel today I decided that when the time is right, I will go to your parents and tell them about the miracle that has happened in your life. I do not doubt that you will be joyously received back at your parental estate, the Castle Hohenburg."

The bell rang. Since they were to remain as guests at the convent until time to return home, Berta and Sigo went with Odelia and the Abbess to the evening service. The chapel service was difficult for Odelia. Her thoughts were spinning around. And that night she could not fall asleep for a very long time. *Another mother? A father? A brother Hugo? A castle on a hill? Leave the Palma Convent? No! There is still so much for me to learn here, and to help with. I want to stay here with my beloved sisters!* As soon as she was sure of that, she was finally able to sleep.

After a few days, Berta and Sigo left to return home. Winter settled over the land,but Berta still could not find the courage to appear before Duke Etichon. She also thought: *Where could Odelia be happier than with the nuns at Palma?*

Hugo Rides to Palma

Years went by, and a new spring had come to the land. A woman dressed as a pilgrim walked up the path to Hohenburg. She looked up at the castle, stood still while thinking, and then looked down to the valley again as if she were doubtful about climbing further. It was Berta. Her steps slowed as she neared the castle gate. Maybe she should turn around. Another guard was there, who did not know Berta. She said: "Announce to the Duchess that her servant, Berta, is here with a message."

The guard waved to a boy who was to announce the visitor to the Duchess. The boy returned quickly and said the stranger was to come with him to the Duchess right away. He led Berta up some steps, knocked on the door, and withdrew.

The door opened. Bereswinde stood there: "Berta!" she cried, and hugged the long-awaited visitor. Immediately she asked: "Is the child alive? How is she?"

Now the long story was begun. Bereswinde was so thankful that the stars of destiny had been kind to her child. She said: "Duke Etichon has ridden out for a few days, but my son, Hugo, is here. I will summon him. Now he shall learn that he has a sister. Hugo has a kind heart. He will be happy."

A squire brought Hugo from the horse stables. He was puzzled as he stepped into the room where the two women sat together. Hugo was a good-looking lad, of stately build, with blonde hair and blue eyes. *Like Odelia*, Berta thought when she greeted him.

At first, Bereswinde began to tell the story. The pain of that bygone time overshadowed her as she told of the birth of his little sister — born blind! Hugo had never known anything about it. He knew about his father's anger, but that he had turned out the baby girl, that bothered him. Bereswinde found her voice again: "And look, Hugo, this dear woman saved the child and raised her as her own."

Bereswinde now asked Berta to continue the story. She reported about their simple, isolated life in the forest and how the child had been well received at the convent in Palma. As she was telling about the miracle of Odelia's baptism, Hugo jumped up, ran to Berta, and cried: "You mean she's alive? I can see her!? She can see me? Mother, I want to have her brought to the castle!"

Berta said: "Then you must make the trip to Palma. Odelia knows that she has a mother here in Hohenburg, and a brother Hugo, and a father who would probably be glad about her today."

"Then I will ride there and get her. Mother, I have a sister!"

Now, Bereswinde had a word to say: "Dear Hugo, yes, we can be glad. But we still do not know how your father will take it. His past offense will be revealed in Odelia. I will talk to him."

Hugo responded: "Yes, you talk to him! But tomorrow I am riding to the Palma Convent. Berta will tell me how to get there. Our Odelia shall no longer live without her family. Perhaps I will be back with Odelia before Father returns!"

Hugo could not be dissuaded. A while ago he had discovered an old double saddle in the tack room, for a rider and a lady sitting side-saddle. He rushed out to get everything ready for the trip. He offered to escort Berta back to her home.

Berta and Bereswinde talked until late in the night. Early the next morning Hugo saddled a strong horse. Bereswinde gave many rich, parting gifts to Berta, and soon they were on their way to the lonely cottage in the forest. Hugo was also curious to meet Odelia's other brother.

Toward evening they came to the old farm cottage. Sigo was outside and looked up in amazement as the horse appeared with a fancy rider and his mother. He hurried to them and held the horse by the bridle. The rider jumped off and helped Berta dismount. Then he went to Sigo, hugged him like an old friend, and said: "I have heard many good things about you from your mother, Berta – how you have been a loyal brother to my sister. I would like to thank you. If everything goes well at Hohenburg, you must come to visit us. I would like to give you one of my horses and teach you how to ride."

Sigo was so surprised by the good-heartedness of the young rider, he had no idea what was happening or how he should answer. Finally, he stammered: "Sir, I am the one who should thank you that you brought my mother home."

Hugo grabbed the young farmer's arm and said: "Please do not call me 'Sir.' My name is Hugo. We are, after all, like brothers!"

Berta's elderly parents had come out of the cottage and were watching this greeting with curiosity. Then Hugo went up to them and expressed his thanks to them as well.

Before Hugo rode away, Sigo offered him a jug of milk to drink. Berta pointed out the way to Palma. Riding fast, Hugo arrived at the convent by the second day. He asked for the Abbess. When he was sitting across from her, he said: "My name is Hugo. I am the son of Duke Etichon and

43

Duchess Bereswinde from Hohenburg. Odelia, my sister, is supposed to be living here in Palma. At my mother's request, I am here to accompany Odelia back to Hohenburg."

Abbess Irmgard was not completely surprised. She admired the cheerful, bold lad, but her heart was heavy. Odelia had become something like the sunshine to those at the convent, even on dreary days. She said to Hugo: "I will send someone to get Odelia right away."

One of the nuns brought her from the scriptorium where she had been working. When she walked in, Hugo stood. He was so overcome by the sight of her that he stood as if rooted to the spot. When Odelia looked at her questioningly, Abbess Irmgard said: "Odelia, this is your brother, Hugo of Hohenburg."

Happiness lit up Odelia's face. She walked to him, took his hands in hers, and said: "Dear brother, how wonderful that you have come!"

Hugo responded: "Dear sister Odelia! I pass along to you a heartfelt greeting from my – from our – mother. She is longing to see you, and our father will also welcome you." His voice broke a little saying those words because, in truth, he was not sure what his father would say. But he continued: "Will you come with me to our castle? My horse has a double saddle so you can ride comfortably. Please, come back to us!"

Odelia bowed her head for a moment as if she were listening to herself. She answered: "Dear brother, for my mother's sake, I will come with you."

The Homecoming

For Odelia it was painful saying farewell to the good nuns at Palma. She had found a second home with them. This is where the great blessing of her baptism had taken place. What would she find at Hohenburg? She was looking forward to seeing her mother, but how would her father receive her? She went alone one last time to the chapel to pray. She put her future destiny into higher hands.

Hugo was waiting with the horse at the convent. Abbess Irmgard said: "Whatever happens, Odelia, the doors of Palma will always be open to you. We go with you in prayer."

Hugo helped Odelia into the saddle. A stamping and whinnying of the horse, a wave and cry from the sisters, and the horse trotted away. One of the nuns had slipped away to the chapel, and suddenly the bell began to ring goodbye.

The sound of the bell faded and then disappeared entirely as the brother and sister rode into the forest. They spent the night at a pilgrim's hostel.

The next day, the Hohenburg castle appeared before Odelia's gaze, high up on a hill. Hugo's heart was heavy as he thought about his father. Odelia asked: "My brother, what is it? You are so silent. All cheerfulness has left you."

He replied: "Let us stop for a short rest! I have to confide something to you. Our father is a hard man, and temperamental. He is not drawn to the Christian God because He represents love and peace. So I am not really sure how he will receive you. Neither I nor my mother has much influence with him."

Odelia thought for a moment, and then replied: "Ride ahead and speak openly with him! I will go on by foot. I will wait for your return at the bottom of the hill."

Hugo rode on ahead. First, he went to his mother and happily reported to her about his lovely sister who had been found again. Overjoyed, Bereswinde said: "Your father is in the armory. I will go and prepare him for the news. Do not keep Odelia waiting any longer. Go and get her!"

Etichon had an ominous expression on his face as the Duchess entered the room. Upon his return he had discovered that Hugo had ridden away and been gone for days. Nobody at the castle seemed to know where he had gone. That made him angry. But the Duchess was so filled with her good news that she did not notice her husband's foul mood. With a light heart, she blurted: "Etichon, our daughter, who was lost, is alive! She got her sight at the convent in Palma. Hugo rode there, and he will soon come and bring her back to us!"

These words had the opposite effect of what Bereswinde had expected. A black shadow crept into the Duke's face, and he burst out in anger: "I do not want that creature to enter my castle. Let her go back from whence she came. If she was meant to live with us, she would have come into the world with her sight. She shall return to the convent!" The poor mother broke out in tears. The Duke left the room with a heavy tread.

In the meantime, on her way to the castle, Odelia had come upon a woodcutter's hut. She saw three mournful children sitting out front. When Odelia walked up to them, the children led her inside to their sick mother. When the ill woman saw the noble figure in a white dress, her fevered mind thought that an angel had come for her soul. Odelia took both her hands. A stream of goodness, health, and strength poured from them into the sick woman. She began to sit up in bed, and she felt her legs and arms begin to quiver with life.

Horse hooves could be heard outside on the path. It was Hugo: "Come, Odelia, Mother is overjoyed at your homecoming, and she is speaking to Father." Odelia said goodbye to the woman and promised to come back.

Brother and sister rode up the hill. As they dismounted in the courtyard, the Duke approached them with a sunken head. Odelia was shocked when he began to yell at her: "Who allowed you to enter my castle against my will?"

Hugo boldly stepped in front of the angry man, and cried: "I did, Father. I allowed it!"

Etichon lifted the knotty, wooden stick he was holding in his hand, and bashed his son's head with it. Hugo fell to the ground, bleeding. Etichon paled when he realized what he had done with his blind act of rage. He let the stick fall, went a few steps backwards, turned, and disappeared into the castle.

Odelia knelt next to Hugo. She tried to stop the bleeding with her handkerchief. With staring eyes he looked at her, and whispered: "Odelia, dear sister!"

At that moment Bereswinde charged out of the castle and collapsed, sobbing, onto the ground next to her children. "Do I have my daughter back only to lose my son!" she cried inconsolably.

Odelia laid her hands on her brother's head and pleaded in her heart for the healing strength of Christ. As it flowed from her arms into her brother, life and death began to struggle with each other inside the youth. Finally, his twitching body sank into a healing slumber.

In the candlelight by Hugo's bed, mother and daughter kept watch the whole night. From time to time, Bereswinde heard the healing words that Odelia spoke over her brother's sleeping form. While her mother fell asleep in her chair, Odelia watched until the morning dawn.

Bereswinde awakened, and soon after, Hugo opened his eyes. In the light, he recognized his mother and sister. In a clear voice, he said: "Mother, I was far away. It was like a bright stream. Then Odelia called me back – now I am here. I am hungry!"

Bereswinde sent one of the maids for milk and some hearty food. Hugo had been won back to this earthly life. Day after day Odelia cared for her brother. Bereswinde admired her and came to love her even more.

His anger broken after his horrible act, Etichon was plagued by nightmares that night. Bereswinde went to his room early the next morning. She forcefully spoke to him: "Etichon, Hugo is alive! Odelia saved him. Let Hugo have one more day of rest in Odelia's care. Go to him tomorrow morning. Ask both of them to forgive you! We have a splendid son and a noble daughter."

So, on the following day, accompanied by Bereswinde, Etichon went to Hugo's room. Odelia was there, putting a healing herb compress on her brother's forehead. Etichon went over to the bed and humbly offered his hand to Odelia. To Hugo he said: "My son! The streak of anger that tore through my arm has badly injured you. I am sorry. It will never happen again. Odelia, I thank you for your help. You may remain at Hohenburg, but please abide by our customs. I am the ruler of this house!" Odelia gazed wordlessly into her father's eyes. She was sorry for him. There was still so much hardness in him. She hoped she could eventually soften his heart toward her.

The Celebration and the Escape

Hugo recuperated under his sister's care. Bereswinde was so glad about the deep friendship between her two children. Etichon avoided his daughter as much as possible. He realized that he needed to change his rough ways when he was around her, but he did not want to do it.

As promised, Odelia went back to the family at the woodcutter's hut and took them bread and healing herbs. The sick mother was soon well again. Odelia also visited elderly people in the area who lived in poverty. She helped them when she could. All of this was not to Etichon's liking. So, he got the idea to marry her off to a German earl who was one of his hunting companions at the time.

After a wild boar hunt, there was to be a big celebration that evening at Hohenburg. The German earl was also invited. Etichon wanted to introduce him to his daughter. Odelia was not even asked if she agreed with her father's plans, but she was still aware of how things stood. This hunting festival was to be combined with a dance which was why all the maidens at the castle had been bidden to attend. Odelia spoke about it to Hugo. He advised her: "In order not to arouse Father's anger, go to the hall for a short time. When the festivities become too wild, you can disappear."

That evening, as Odelia stood at the entrance of the great hall and heard the bellowing revelers and saw the already out of control merrymaking, she stepped back in fear. She hurried back to her room. She had made her decision: She would escape and go back to Palma. She bundled up a few of her things. The castle gate was open, and the guard was at the celebration. She did not want to say anything to her mother or brother so they could not be blamed. She fled out the unguarded gate, down the hill. She rested for a short time at the woodcutter's cottage and asked the woman for a simple dress in exchange for her festive clothing. The woman was amazed, but willing, and she promised to keep quiet about Odelia's visit. Then Odelia disappeared into the dark forest. The moon shone brightly, allowing her to travel that night.

In all the tumult of the party, Odelia's absence had not been noticed, and Etichon was drunk with wine. The next day it was noon by the time he and the other revelers had slept off their drunkenness. Etichon asked after Odelia. Nobody knew where she was. Bereswinde assumed that she had gone to visit the poor and sick in the valley. But when she had not yet returned on the second day, Etichon suspected she had fled. He asked Hugo if he knew where his sister was.

"No, I don't know where she is!"

Etichon lashed out in anger: "I will bring her back from Palma. She must submit to my will!"

On the third day, Etichon and Ulrich, his trusted friend, rode away from the castle with two hunting dogs. The dogs picked up the scent and started heading south. Etichon turned in that direction. On the way he stopped to visit various farms on his vast estate because he was sure that he would find Odelia at Palma.

Odelia had a good head start. She came into the area of present day Basel in Switzerland. Where the Birs River flows, she saw a lovely, forested landscape. She crossed the river at a shallow place and directed her steps to a large farm. There the tired pilgrim could rest. Odelia inquired about the owner of the farm and surrounding lands. The answer was: "Duke Etichon of Hohenburg is our master."

Odelia was shocked, and she became very fearful. Suddenly she knew that her escape had been discovered and her father was looking for her. She must get away from here! He would certainly come to this farm, and he had good hunting dogs. So, Odelia fled past the village of Arlesheim, up into the forest where cliffs and caves would offer some shelter.

It was certainly just in time. The Duke, Ulrich, and the hounds arrived at the farm and were told that just a short time ago a young, blonde pilgrim had rested there. The dogs soon found the fresh scent and led the men into the forest. In the meantime, Odelia had climbed up a rocky outcropping and hidden herself inside a cave. She pleaded to her guardian angel for protection.

As the hounds followed the scent upwards, a shining figure appeared in front of the cave. The dogs yelped and seemed afraid to climb up the rocks. The Duke looked up and saw the angel. As he was staring, one of the dogs above him loosened a large rock. It rolled down and hit Etichon on his forehead with such great force that he was benumbed and fell to the ground. Suddenly, he saw the shining figure float down to him from the cave and surround him with light. It was as if his soul were penetrated with fire, and he was shaken. He was flaming inside, as if all his anger was being burned away.

That is how Ulrich found him, injured and unconscious. He called the dogs and went for help. The Duke was carried back to the farm on a wide plank. The dogs were chained up. The farmer's wife dressed the Duke's head wound and put herb compresses on it. They hardly noticed when

he awakened, he lay so silently in his pain. During the days that followed, his soul went through a deep change. His mind became clear again, but he barely spoke. When Etichon was able to sit his horse again, Ulrich rode quietly with him back home to Hohenburg.

Etichon did not speak to anyone for many days. Bereswinde, Hugo, and all the castle attendants saw that a great transformation had come over the Duke. He brooded, but showed neither impatience nor the least bit of anger.

During this time, one evening a traveling Irish monk came to the castle and asked for shelter for the night. Such monks commonly wandered the regions of Alsace and the Vosges Mountains. They brought the message of Christ, founded monasteries, and built hermitages. It was an elderly, wise monk who greeted Bereswinde. He called himself Irmo. The Duchess confided her worries and sorrows to him. She brought the monk into Etichon's room, where he was lying on his bed.

The Duke gave his hand to Irmo and indicated a chair for him to sit. Bereswinde left the two alone. Irmo stayed many hours with the Duke. Etichon opened up his fearful soul to the monk and asked him to stay longer at the castle, to help him and teach him.

Those living at the castle wondered if Odelia had gone back to Palma. Irmo advised: "Let her go her own way!"

Odelia Reconciles with Her Father

What had happened to Odelia at the cave? When she no longer heard the barking dogs, she found the courage to come out of her hiding place. Then she saw that they were carrying her father away. It was all so puzzling. Not knowing what else to do, she stayed in the cave for a few more days, living on the berries and herbs of the forest. Once when she was silently praying, she heard a clear inner voice: "Odelia, you may return home. Your father's mind has turned to the good. He needs you!"

This inner experience was so strong that Odelia decided to get underway the very next day. Walking through fields and forest quieted her restless soul. When she got close to the woodcutter's hut, she did not go inside. She did not want her beautiful clothing back. Soon she was standing again in front of the Hohenburg Castle. The guard whom Odelia liked showed great happiness. She said to him: "Don't make any noise! I will find them myself."

She went unnoticed to her room and put on the white wool dress she had worn in Palma. Then she climbed the stairs to her mother's rooms. Upon hearing the knock, her mother opened the door and hugged Odelia with a shout of joy. She told Odelia about her father's accident and his wonderful change of heart. Odelia heard about Irmo, the wise monk from Ireland, who spent time with Etichon every day. Odelia said to her mother: "So, let me go to Father alone! Everything will be all right. I know it!"

The door to Etichon's room was not latched. Nothing stirred when she knocked softly. Gently she pushed open the door and saw her father standing by the window, deep in thought. She stood on the threshold in her white dress. Her father turned around slowly, opened his arms wide, and walked toward her: "Odelia!" He spoke her name for the first time.

As he held her close, Odelia felt her cheeks moistened with her father's tears. Gently, she stepped back and looked at him: "Dearest Father, we travel many false paths and go through much suffering until the love and strength of Christ can reach us. His peace will now reign over us. Come, Father, let us go to Mother!"

In the meantime, Hugo had gone to Bereswinde when he heard about Odelia's return. His mother said to him: "Stay with me! Odelia has gone to your father. We must not interrupt their reunion."

Hugo said: "So she didn't go back to Palma. Will she stay with us?"

"We haven't talked about that yet."

Footsteps were heard on the stairs. Odelia walked in with her father. Joyfully, Hugo greeted his sister, and there was Etichon, smiling, his eyes gleaming with gladness. But then, Etichon spoke: "Bring Irmo, our guest! He should have a part in our happiness. Hugo, you will find him up in the tower room."

The Tower Room

Irmo the monk was busy turning the tower room into a chapel. A small table with a red cloth served as an altar. Three candlesticks decorated it. A cross with a woven sun-ring stood in the middle, surrounded by colorful rocks and a crystal, also a dried rose with many thorns. Leaning on each candlestick was a wooden tablet with the carved letters J – C – H. Irmo had prepared all of this in the last few days.

Hugo knocked on the heavy wooden door. When Irmo opened it, Hugo blurted out: "Odelia is back! She has reconciled with Father. Come, Irmo, we are all in Mother's rooms. You have to be there!"

Soon all five people were sitting together. Irmo told stories about Ireland, the faraway green isle, and how the revelations of Christ were received by the Druid priests. He went on: "Today there are hundreds of monasteries in Ireland. Many missionaries like me go overseas to spread the good news of Christ. From the south, the brothers work with the Roman Church, because Europe should become a refuge of Christianity. Basically, all people want to embody the spirit of neighborly love."

So, Brother Irmo instructed the Duke and his family. Then he said: "I have set up a small chapel in the tower room. This evening I would like to hold a service with all of you there to celebrate Odelia's homecoming. Your faith must be given nourishment!"

"Just like the horses need oats!" Hugo said.

Bright, soft laughter sounded forth from Odelia. It was her first real laughter since she had come home to Hohenburg.

As a result of his accident, Duke Etichon was no longer able to hunt.

Now, he would often sit with Irmo in the tower room. With Hugo's help, Irmo had built a harp like the one he had brought from Ireland. He gave it to Odelia, and she sang the Irish songs she had learned at Palma. Gradually, the other residents of the castle started taking part in the services in the tower room.

One day Etichon said to Odelia: "The tower room is much too small. I am going to build a chapel onto the castle. Then people from the valley will be able to attend Irmo's services also."

Many hands got busy, and in half a year, the chapel stood as an addition to the castle. Odelia had an idea: She wanted to found a convent at Hohenburg similar to the one at Palma.

The Castle and Two Convents

Building the chapel had awakened a desire in Etichon to keep building. When Odelia told him about her idea to build a convent at Hohenburg, he was ready to help. Large rocks were broken from the cliffs and carried to Hohenburg in ox-drawn wagons. Already at Hohenburg was the remnant of an old Celtic wall from a Celtic holy site from many, many years ago. Etichon said: "These stones will serve as the greater portion of what we need for the convent's walls."

And Irmo added: "The old Celtic Druids would be happy to know that these stones will hear Christian songs!"

Hugo had not forgotten the little cottage in the forest and Sigo, but the building project was taking most of his time. Together with his father and Irmo, he had taken on the task of overseeing the building of the convent. Instead of hunting, they were all now building! As winter came upon them, the convent chapel stood finished, and some living quarters had been built onto the castle. Thus, a convent was integrated into the Hohenburg castle, and Odelia could begin to work on bringing about a smaller version of Palma.

One spring day, when the snow had melted, Hugo decided to take a day's ride to the forest cottage and look in on Berta and Sigo. Sigo had often dreamed of owning a horse. But he thought that the young Duke could not possibly have time to concern himself with a farmer. Imagine his and Berta's happiness when Hugo rode up to their cottage.

Hugo learned that the grandparents had died during the past winter. Sigo and Berta were now running the little farm by themselves. After Hugo told them about all the changes at Hohenburg, he made them an offer:

"A woodcutter and his family live below the castle. They would rather have a small farm. We would like to have both of you at Hohenburg. Sigo would make a good foreman, and Berta could help Bereswinde and Odelia with their duties. A good horse has been waiting for you for a long time, Sigo. I will buy your little farm and rent it to the woodcutter."

Hugo could hardly believe how quickly the two of them said yes to his offer. Sigo was tired of the isolation of the forest. Berta missed Bereswinde and Odelia. So, the business was concluded.

Odelia was now the Abbess of Hohenburg Convent. Gradually, they began to take in sick people. Odelia was able to call forth much healing energy. More and more young women declared themselves willing to enter the convent and care for the sick.

When Etichon felt that he would not live much longer, he gave the castle to Odelia. Hugo took care of the many acres of land. With Hugo's help, Sigo learned how to ride and grew into a very competent estate foreman. Berta and Bereswinde stood by Odelia to help however they could. Irmo, the priest, remained loyal to Odelia and the convent. His Christian message radiated far in the region.

After Duke Etichon passed away, Bereswinde donated money to build a second convent in the valley below Hohenburg. Built under the supervision of Hugo and Sigo, it was called Niedermuenster. Here, also, the sick and handicapped were taken in. Odelia divided her time between the two convents, helping and healing. She was loved and honored by the people. Slowly, the name Hohenburg was heard less often, and people started calling it *Odelianberg*.

And that is how it is known to this day. For centuries now Odelianberg has been a place that radiates mercy and Christian charity.

Made in the USA
San Bernardino, CA
20 February 2018